# ULTIMATE ACTIVITY HANDBOOK

## FACTS, STATS, GAMES — AND MORE!

ORCHARD BOOKS

First published in Great Britain in 2018 by The Watts Publishing Group

3 5 7 9 10 8 6 4 2

HASBRO and its logo, NERF is a trademark of Hasbro and is used with permission.
© 2018 Hasbro. All Rights Reserved.

A CIP catalogue record for this book is available from the British Library

ISBN 978 1 40835 852 8

Printed and bound in China

Orchard Books
An imprint of Hachette Children's Group
Part of The Watts Publishing Group Limited
Carmelite House
50 Victoria Embankment
London EC4Y 0DZ

An Hachette UK Company
www.hachette.co.uk
www.hachettechildrens.co.uk

Adult supervision is recommended for all cooking activities, and when
glue, paint, scissors and other sharp points are in use.

Always get adult permission when playing with blasters indoors or outdoors.

CAUTION: Do not aim blasters at eyes or face. TO AVOID INJURY: Use only
with official NERF darts. Other darts may not meet safety standards.
Do not modify darts or dart blaster.

# IT'S NERF OR NOTHIN'!

# NERF

## ULTIMATE ACTIVITY HANDBOOK

IT'S NERF OR NOTHIN'!

4

# WELCOME TO THE

# NERF

## ULTIMATE ACTIVITY HANDBOOK

Packed with all the facts and stats
about the latest Nerf blasters, you can
find out everything you need to know
to become a Nerf expert.

Plus, there are tons of activities, game ideas
and challenges to take on with your friends.
So grab your blaster and get started!

# FACTS AND STATS

## N-STRIKE MODULUS MEDIATOR
Length: 35.6 cm
Height: 22.9 cm

**BARREL**

**ACCESSORIES**
Barrel: 38 cm x 28 cm
Stock: 31.8 cm x 16.5 cm

**SLAM-FIRE BLASTING**

**STOCK**

**BARREL AND STOCK ATTACHMENT POINTS**

**PUMP-ACTION, CLIP-FED BLASTER**

MEDIATOR

5

NERF®

**CREATE THE MEDIATOR XL BLASTER!**

**TACTICAL RAILS**

[N-STRIKE]

# MODULUS

SYSTEM · SYSTÈME · SISTEMA

# FACTS AND STATS

CYCLONESHOCK

**N-STRIKE MEGA CYCLONESHOCK**
Length: 41.2 cm
Height: 25.3 cm

LOAD THE DRUM WITH SIX MEGA WHISTLER DARTS FOR EASY FIRING!

FIRES 6 DARTS
WITHOUT RELOADING

FIRES MEGA
WHISTLER DARTS
UP TO 27M

ROTATING
6-DART DRUM

N-STRIKE®

MEGA

# FACTS AND STATS

**10-DART CLIP**

ACCUSTRIKE NERF MEGA DARTS ARE THE MOST ACCURATE NERF DARTS!

**FOLDING BIPOD**

## N-STRIKE MEGA ACCUSTRIKE THUNDERHAWK

Length: 1 metre – the longest Nerf blaster!

Height: 39.1cm

**ACCUSTRIKE NERF MEGA DARTS**

N-STRIKE® MEGA

# FACTS AND STATS

## N-STRIKE MEGA TRI-BREAK

Length: 31.8 cm
Height: 22.9 cm

BREAK-OPEN BARREL HOLDS THREE NERF MEGA WHISTLER DARTS!

**BREAK-OPEN
BARREL**

TRI-BREAK

**MEGA WHISTLER
DARTS SCREAM
THROUGH THE AIR!**

# N-STRIKE®
# MEGA

13

# DART ZONE

Depending on your mission it's always important to make sure you're using the right Nerf Dart for the job.

Whether you need power, distance, accuracy or something to hunt Zombies – Nerf has got you covered!

## NERF N-STRIKE ELITE DARTS

**USE FOR:** All-round performance

**USE ON:** All Nerf N-Strike blasters, except Mega

# NERF N-STRIKE ELITE ACCUSTRIKE DARTS

**USE FOR:** Accuracy

**USE ON:** All Nerf N-Strike blasters, except Mega

# NERF N-STRIKE ZOMBIE STRIKE DARTS

**USE FOR:** Hunting zombies

**USE ON:** All Nerf N-Strike blasters, except Mega

# NERF N-STRIKE MEGA DARTS

**USE FOR:** Heavy-duty missions

**USE ON:** Nerf N-Strike Mega Blasters

# RATE IT!

Now you've read about some super-cool blasters, which is your favourite? Give each blaster a score below to find out!

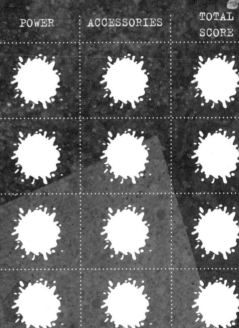

| NAME: | LOOKS | POWER | ACCESSORIES | TOTAL SCORE |
|---|---|---|---|---|
| N-STRIKE MODULUS MEDIATOR | | | | |
| N-STRIKE MEGA CYCLONESHOCK | | | | |
| N-STRIKE MEGA ACCUSTRIKE THUNDERHAWK | | | | |
| N-STRIKE MEGA TRI-BREAK | | | | |

WINNER:

-----------------------------

# TOP TACTICS

**A battle is all about tactics! Read our three best defence and attack techniques before your next outing on the battlefield.**

## STRIKE!

1. Keep your darts close by for quick reloading! Use a flip clip to give you extra time.

2. Choose your moment! Watch what your opponents are doing and strike when you see a weakness in their formation.

3. Be confident! When you have made the decision to attack, stay with it! If you're unsure, your enemies will pick up on it.

## DEFEND!

1. Keep your eyes open! Remember, enemies can be lurking almost anywhere.

2. Keep quiet! If your opponents can hear you, they'll be able to fire at you.

3. Keep your shield on your blaster. Better safe than sorry!

17

# ARSENAL CHEST

The best blasters have lots of accessories. Make this cool chest to keep everything in order and close to hand should your enemy strike!

## YOU WILL NEED:

Plain lidded box
(around 40.5 x 32 x 25cm)
Scissors or a craft knife
Glue
Cereal box
Three pieces of
elastic 9cm long
Shoe box
Paint

Cut on dotted lines

-----------✂

## STEP 1

Take your cereal box and tape up the lid. Place the box on its side and use scissors or a craft knife to cut off one of the sides. You should now have a box with an opening on one of the thin sides. Add glue to the front or back of the cereal box and glue it to the inside of your lidded box at one of the shorter ends. Make sure the hole you have made is at the top as this will be your flip clip and darts storage.

## STEP 2

Using your scissors or craft knife, make three sets of two holes along one of the long sides of your box. Each pair of holes should be 5cm apart.

Now take a piece of elastic and make a knot on one end. Thread the other end through one of the holes going from the outside in. Thread the other end through the next hole and tie a knot so that the elastic lies flat against the side of the box. Do the same with the other two pieces of elastic to create three loops. These loops can hold your pivot grip, proximity barrel or distance scope.

## STEP 3

Remove the lid of your shoe box and glue the bottom to the inside of your box. Place it on the opposite side to the cereal box to leave a space in the middle. The shoe box can be used for smaller accessories.

## STEP 4

Now you have the structure of your chest, it's time to make it look the part! Paint your chest white inside and out as a base colour. Don't forget the lid! Now add some colour and decorations – you could match the colours of your favourite blaster. Why not paint on your initials so everyone knows this is your arsenal!

# OPERATION STEALTH

**Play this game with friends to see who is the stealthiest!**

## YOU WILL NEED:

Paper
Sticky tape

## HOW TO PLAY:

**1.** Copy or cut out the playing pieces and place them on square 1.

**2.** Copy the wheel, right, on to a piece of A4 paper and stick it to the wall.

**3.** Standing at least three metres away from the wheel, use your blaster to hit the wheel then move that number along the board.

**4.** When you land on Long Range, Strike and Defend, or Stealth Ops squares, you must complete the mission before you can move to the next square.

## PLAYING PIECES

**1**

**2**

**STEALTH OPS**
The other players close their eyes and count to 10 while you hide in the room. If they can't spot you without moving, go forwards three spaces.

**4**

**5**

**6**

**STRIKE AND DEFEND**
The other players stand at least 3m away and fire a dart. If you can knock the darts out of the air, go forwards three spaces.

**8**

**14**

**13**

**12**

**10**

**YOUR BLASTER IS JAMMED!**
Go back one space.

**YOUR LINE OF VISION IS BLOCKED.**
Go back one space.

**16**

**RELOADED IN RECORD TIME!**
Go forwards one space.

**18**

**LONG RANGE**
Stand as far away from a door as possible. You have one chance to fire a dart through the door. If you do, go forwards three spaces.

**20**

**STRIKE AND DEFEND**
Use a door as a shield. If you can hit your fellow players without getting hit yourself, go forwards three spaces.

**22**

**STEALTH OPS**
If you can name the exact number of darts the rest of the players have loaded into their blasters now, go forwards three spaces.

**28**

**LONG RANGE**
Stand far away from a window. You have one chance to fire a dart through the open window. If you do, go forwards three spaces.

**26**

**IT'S NEARLY MISSION COMPLETE!**
Go forwards one space.

**24**

**YOU LET DOWN YOUR GUARD TOO EARLY!**
Miss a turn.

# TRICK SHOTS

Use your favourite blaster and see if you can complete all three trick shots!

## IN TRAINING

Trick shots look cool for a reason – they've usually taken the person hours of practice to perfect! Don't give up if you don't get your shot right first time, keep trying – it'll be worth it!

## MAKE IT COUNT

When you've only got one shot left, you've got to make it count. Place two paper cups on top of each other. Place a small empty container on top. Use the last shot in your blaster to knock the top paper cup out of the way so the container falls into the bottom cup.

## LONG DISTANCE RELATIONSHIP

Get a friend to take two
balls (a football and tennis ball
are ideal) and walk at least
10 metres away. Ask your friend to
keep the balls at their side until you
shout 'Go!'. It's up to your friend to
decide how they hold the balls (to
the side, above their head etc) and
up to you to blast them as
quickly as possible!

## ON TARGET

Place a paper cup on its
side on top of a pile of books.
Find a position with a similar
height (behind a chair or table)
and see if you can fire a single
dart into the cup. To make it even
more of a challenge, try firing a
dart into an empty
drinks bottle!

# IT'S NERF™
# OR NOTHIN'!

# PICK YOUR BATTLEFIELD

Would you rather battle in the heat of
the desert or cold Arctic tundra?
Take the quiz to find out!

## Q1 WOULD YOU RATHER BE ...

☐ A) Too hot
☐ B) Too cold
☐ C) Too wet
☐ D) Too dry

## Q2 ANIMALS ARE ...

☐ A) Amazing, the more the better
☐ B) Great, but could get in the way
☐ C) Bad news, they distract you
     from your mission
☐ D) Dangerous probably

## Q3 WHAT'S YOUR MISSION STYLE?

☐ A) I'm all action and ready
     for anything
☐ B) I plan carefully but like
     extreme situations
☐ C) Laid back – I keep my eyes
     open and my blaster close
☐ D) I like to go solo

## Q4 WHAT'S YOUR FAVOURITE STYLE OF BLASTER?

☐ A) The bigger the better –
     with lots of darts
☐ B) Something trustworthy
     and lightweight
☐ C) A small, hand-held blaster
     I can hide in my coat
☐ D) A blaster with lots of
     different functions

## Q5 WHAT'S THE BEST ACCESSORY?

- ☐ A] A utility belt to hold my darts and modifications
- ☐ B] A big coat for warmth with lots of pockets for rations
- ☐ C] Dark glasses, so no one can spot your next target
- ☐ D] A water bottle for energy

## Q6 ON YOUR MISSION, FRIENDS ARE ...

- ☐ A] Welcome. Sharing your adventures is great
- ☐ B] OK, as long as they stick to the plan
- ☐ C] All around you
- ☐ D] Nowhere to be seen

### MOSTLY AS
### JUNGLE WARFARE

You're an adventurer who's ready for anything. The jungle would suit you as there's always loads to explore and discover, plus it's really exciting, too!

### MOSTLY BS
### ARCTIC ADVENTURER

You like to take your missions to the extremes. The harder, the better! Your dream destination would be the North Pole – just watch out for polar bears!

### MOSTLY CS
### AWESOME URBANITE

The city is the place to be for you. You love being able to sneak undercover and blend in with your surroundings. You are always ready for the next top secret mission.

### MOSTLY DS
### DESERTED

Sweltering in a hot desert with no one around for miles sounds like your idea of fun. You and your blaster would make an excellent team as you cross the wide open terrain.

# RACE TO THE

Speed and agility are vital for success in battle. Find the path through this maze as quickly as possible.

**START**

# FINISH

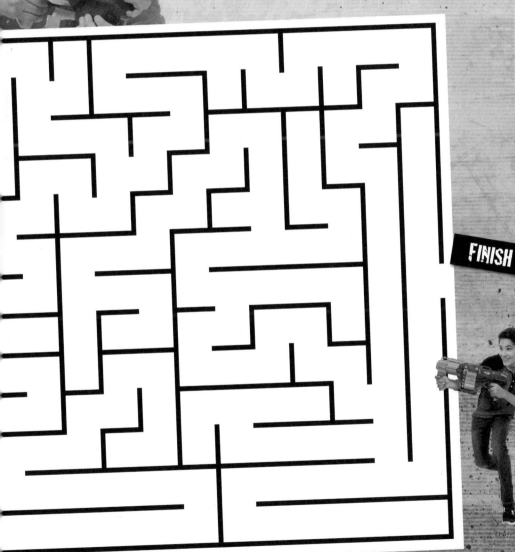

FINISH

Answer on page 127

# SPECIAL BLASTERS

**The best blasters are personal! Customise the blasters below in your own unique colours and style. Would you add any accessories?**

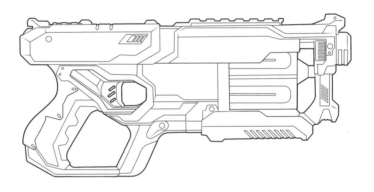

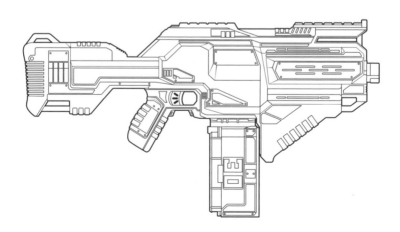

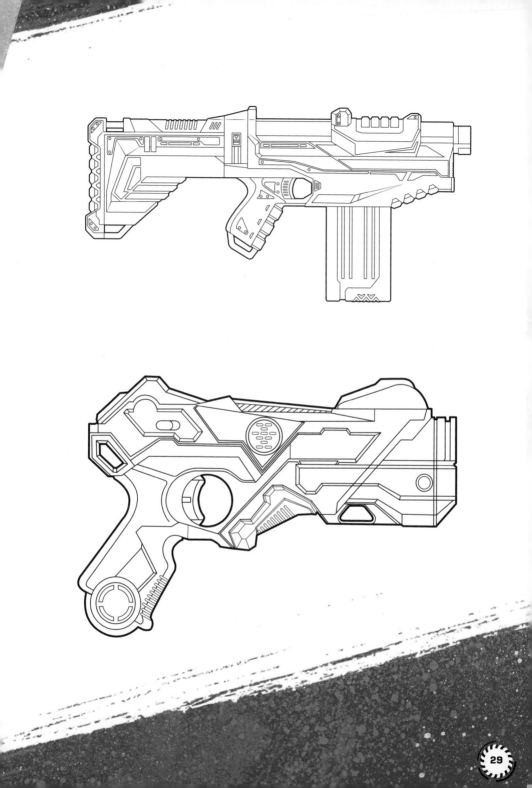

# GAME IDEAS

## Gather your friends and your blasters and try these fun games!

### CAPTURE THE FLAG

**PLAYERS:** 6 or more
**GOAL:** To capture your enemy's flag and return it safely to your base. Protect your own flag.

### HOW TO PLAY

- Choose a large area to play – the more obstacles, such as tables or trees, the better
- Set up two bases and place the flags in clear sight – make sure everyone knows where the flags are
- Each team starts at their flag. When the game begins each team must try and capture the other flag and bring it back to their base
- The first team to safely bring the flag back wins!

### RULES

- If you are hit by a dart you are out of play and can't use your blaster. You can only move when a teammate taps you on the shoulder
- Only one person can hold the flag – it can't be passed to another player
- If the player holding the flag is hit, they must hand the flag back so it returns to base. The other team can't steal the flag until it is back in place
- If everyone on your team has been hit, you lose!
- If you run out of darts, scavenge for more!

**TOP TIPS!**
Travel in pairs so if someone is hit, their teammate can tap them.
Always have someone protecting the flag carrier!

## PROTECT THE VIP

**PLAYERS:** 5 or more
**GOAL:** To take out the opposing team's VIP or safely move the VIP to the evacuation point

### HOW TO PLAY

- Choose teams and decide who will be the VIP

- Decide if you want the VIP to have a blaster or be unarmed – it is more of a challenge if they are unarmed!

- Choose a starting point, an evacuation point and a safe point for your VIP – it's good if these are quite far apart

- When the game starts, it is the job of the team without a VIP to capture them. The team with the VIP must safely transport them to the evacuation point

- The team who succeeds in their mission wins!

### RULES

- If the VIP is hit, that team loses

- If you are hit, you are out of the game

- Each player only gets one clip of darts

- If your clip runs out you are out of the game. But if your last dart takes a player out, you may steal their blaster and play on

- The VIP can't be left unguarded

## FREE FOR ALL

**PLAYERS:** 2 or more
**GOAL:** To be the last player standing

### HOW TO PLAY

- Choose your game zone – make sure everyone knows what is in and out of play

- Have one person hide the darts and another hide the blasters around the game zone – ideally this should be someone not playing

- Set up special items around your game zone such as health packs, extra darts or extra blasters. These can only be used once per game, so make sure you shout to let everyone know when they have been used

- When you are ready to play, all players must stand together. Count down from five and then start searching

- The player left standing at the end of play is the winner!

### RULES

- No teaming up! This is an individual game

- Each player can be hit five times before they are eliminated – health packs restore one life

- If you eliminate another player, you can steal their blasters, darts or other items – but only the person who has eliminated them can steal!

# MISSING BLASTERS

The blasters are out! Can you find the blasters in the wordsearch below?

| C | S | U | R | G | E | F | I | R | E | T | T | L | X |
|---|---|---|---|---|---|---|---|---|---|---|---|---|---|
| B | J | A | T | R | O | T | A | I | D | E | M | V | T |
| C | R | T | A | F | I | R | E | S | T | R | I | K | E |
| N | B | T | P | O | P | Z | I | P | R | R | T | C | T |
| T | K | X | E | K | G | V | E | W | O | S | A | O | X |
| A | S | R | Y | R | O | N | P | T | O | U | C | H | U |
| V | R | O | P | O | S | T | P | T | P | R | Y | S | E |
| S | X | A | T | N | T | U | T | E | E | T | B | E | R |
| T | N | P | T | O | R | T | V | Z | R | T | T | N | J |
| R | Q | T | A | S | T | O | Y | B | V | X | D | O | S |
| Y | L | T | I | E | M | N | A | R | Y | T | U | L | F |
| F | T | D | T | P | E | I | F | N | U | I | Q | C | N |
| E | K | L | T | R | U | R | W | Q | U | W | E | Y | A |
| T | X | I | Y | K | R | E | U | T | A | B | L | C | R |

**CYCLONESHOCK**  **KRONOS**
**DISRUPTOR**  **STRYFE**
**TROOPER**  **SURGEFIRE**
**FIRESTRIKE**  **MEDIATOR**

Answer on page 127

# SPOT THE
# DIFFERENCE

Can you spot five differences between the two pictures below? Colour a blaster for each one you find!

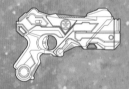

Answer on page 127

# FACTS AND STATS

### N-STRIKE ELITE INFINUS
Length: 64.5 cm
Height: 34.8cm

NO NEED TO REMOVE THE DRUM TO RELOAD – LOAD AND FIRE IN BATTLE!

**SPEED-LOAD TECHNOLOGY**

FULLY
MOTORISED
BLASTER

LOAD DARTS
WITHOUT
REMOVING THE
DRUM

# FACTS AND STATS

### N-STRIKE ELITE SURGEFIRE

Length: 45.7 cm
Height: 20.3 cm

NERF

ELITE

**LAUNCH DARTS UP TO 27 METRES!**

**15-DART ROTATING DRUM**

**SLAM-FIRE ACTION**

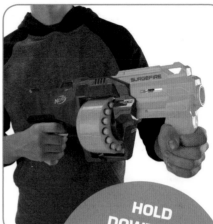

**HOLD DOWN THE TRIGGER AND MOVE THE GRIP BACK AND FORWARDS TO SLAM-FIRE ALL DARTS!**

SURGEFIRE

**PUMP-ACTION BLASTING**

N-STRIKE ELITE

# FACTS AND STATS

**N-STRIKE ELITE DISRUPTOR**
Length: 31.5 cm
Height: 22 cm

**QUICK-DRAW BLASTER**

**CHECK THE INDICATOR ON THE N-STRIKE DISRUPTOR – IF IT'S ORANGE THE BLASTER IS PRIMED AND READY TO FIRE!**

**6-DART ROTATING DRUM**

**DISRUPTOR**

NERF

**SLAM-FIRE ACTION**

N-STRIKE ELITE

# FACTS AND STATS

## N-STRIKE ELITE DELTA TROOPER

Length: 69.5cm
Height: 25.4cm

ATTACH THE STOCK TO STABILISE SHOTS

**BUILT-IN ATTACHMENT POINTS FOR CUSTOMISING**

N-STRIKE

# ELITE

**ATTACHABLE STOCK AND BARREL EXTENSION**

.TA TROOPER

**12-DART CLIP**

ADD THE BARREL EXTENSION FOR DISTANCE TARGETING

# FACTS AND STATS

## N-STRIKE ELITE FIRESTRIKE

Length: 31.5 cm
Height: 22 cm

**FIRES DARTS UP TO 27 METRES**

**LIGHT BEAM CAN ZERO IN ON TARGETS UP TO 4.5 METRES AWAY!**

**SINGLE SHOT
BLASTER**

**LIGHT BEAM
TARGETING**

FIRESTRIKE

**STORAGE
FOR TWO
DARTS**

N-STRIKE ELITE

# FACTS AND STATS

## N-STRIKE ELITE STRYFE

Length: 33cm
Height: 17.8cm

ACCELERATION TRIGGER POWERS UP THE BLASTER'S MOTOR TO LAUNCH DARTS AT SPEED!

**ACCELERATION TRIGGER**

**ONE-HANDED BLASTING**

STRYFE

NERF

NERF

**QUICK-RELOAD CLIP**

N-STRIKE ELITE

# TARGET PRACTICE

**Test your shooting skills with these targets – can you blast them all?**

## HOW TO PLAY:

1. Choose an area to practise your skills, outside is best

2. Copy or cut out the targets and choose a spot for each target – try different distances or heights

3. Secure the targets with sticky tape or drawing pins

4. Select your starting point and then get practising!

**TOP TIP!**
To get the best distance, hold your blaster at a 45 degree angle and be aware of which way, and how strongly, the wind is blowing.

# TARGETS

# SECRET CODE

When you are on undercover missions it is always best to communicate in code – you never know who might intercept your message! Use the symbols below to crack the secret message.

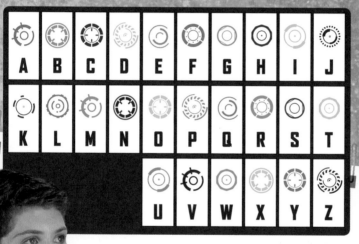

| A | B | C | D | E | F | G | H | I | J |
|---|---|---|---|---|---|---|---|---|---|
| K | L | M | N | O | P | Q | R | S | T |
| | | | | U | V | W | X | Y | Z |

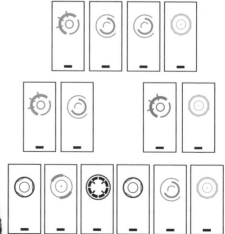

Answer on page 127

# TRUE OR FALSE?

How much have you learnt about the blasters so far? Take the quiz and find out!

## Q1. HOW LONG IS THE MODULUS MEDIATOR?

- ☐ 35.6 cm
- ☐ 37.2 cm
- ☐ 33.8 cm

## Q2. WHICH IS THE LONGEST NERF BLASTER?

- ☐ N-Strike Disruptor
- ☐ N-Strike Mega AccuStrike Thunderhawk
- ☐ N-Strike Mega Cycloneshock

## Q3. WHICH BLASTER CAN BE USED ONE-HANDED?

- ☐ N-Strike Elite Firestrike
- ☐ N-Strike Elite Infinus
- ☐ N-Strike Elite Stryfe

## Q4. THE N-STRIKE SURGEFIRE HAS A 15-DART ROTATING DRUM

- ☐ TRUE
- ☐ FALSE

Answers on page 127

49

# TOP SCORER

**Grab your friends and play this game to decide who will be top scorer!**

## PLAYERS: 4 or more

## HOW TO PLAY

- Decide whether you will play this game inside or outside
- Decide a start and a finish point – ideally they will be a good distance apart
- One player is chosen to be the hunter and chooses their favourite blaster
- The rest of the players choose a blaster and stick a score on to their top
- The hunter turns around and counts to 30 while the rest of the players spread out and choose a hiding spot
- Once the hunter counts to 30, they can turn around and the game begins
- Each player must make it to the finishing point without being hit by the hunter
- Once all players have been hit or made it to the finish point, the game is over
- The hunter must add up the points of all the players he has blasted, while the players who made it to the finish add up their total points. Whoever has the most points wins!

## RULES

- If the hunter is hit five times before all players reach the finish, the game is over
- If a player is hit by the hunter, they are eliminated from the game

50

# TARGETS

# DISCOVER YOUR PERFECT BLASTER

**Answer the questions below to discover which blaster is your ideal match!**

## Q1 THE MOST IMPORTANT THING ABOUT YOUR BLASTER IS ...

- ☐ A) Its power
- ☐ B) Its speed
- ☐ C) Its accuracy
- ☐ D) Its adaptability

## Q2 ON A MISSION, YOU ...

- ☐ A) Are first in line – you love the action!
- ☐ B) Blast first, ask questions later
- ☐ C) Take your time and make every shot count
- ☐ D) Plan, plan, plan!

## Q3 WHAT SIZE BLASTER DO YOU LIKE?

- ☐ A) The bigger the better!
- ☐ B) Quite big but with lots of darts
- ☐ C) Medium-sized
- ☐ D) A blaster that can change to suit me!

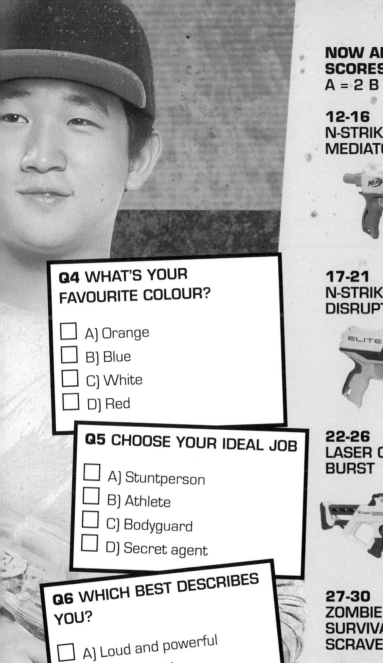

## NOW ADD UP YOUR SCORES!
A = 2 B = 3 C = 4 D = 5

### 12-16
**N-STRIKE MODULUS MEDIATOR**

### 17-21
**N-STRIKE ELITE DISRUPTOR**

### 22-26
**LASER OPS DELTA BURST**

### 27-30
**ZOMBIE STRIKE SURVIVAL SYSTEM SCRAVENGER**

## Q4 WHAT'S YOUR FAVOURITE COLOUR?

- ☐ A) Orange
- ☐ B) Blue
- ☐ C) White
- ☐ D) Red

## Q5 CHOOSE YOUR IDEAL JOB

- ☐ A) Stuntperson
- ☐ B) Athlete
- ☐ C) Bodyguard
- ☐ D) Secret agent

## Q6 WHICH BEST DESCRIBES YOU?

- ☐ A) Loud and powerful
- ☐ B) Quick and fun
- ☐ C) Calm under pressure
- ☐ D) Clever and confident

# Create your own
# BLASTER

Now you have found out which blaster is most suited to you, design your own here. What accessories would you add to your blaster?

# RACE TO THE FINISH

See who can make it to the finish the quickest in this fun game!

## COUNTERS

## YOU WILL NEED:

Counters
A die

**PLAYERS: 2 or more**

### HOW TO PLAY

- Each player chooses a counter and places it on the start box
- Take it in turns to roll the die and move forwards the number of spaces
- If you land on a box with a blaster, move up the board
- If you land on a space with a dart, move down the board
- The first player to reach the finish wins!

## IT'S NERF OR NOTHIN'!

| 47 | 48 | 49 | 50 | **FINISH** |
|----|----|----|----|----|
| 46 | 45 | 44 | 43 | 42 | 41 |
| 35 | 3 | 7 | 38 | 3 | 40 |
| 3 | 3 | 32 | 31 | 30 | 9 |
| 23 | 24 | 25 | 26 | 27 | 28 |
| 2 | 21 | 20 | | 8 | 17 |
| | 12 | 1 | 4 | 15 | 16 |
| 10 | 9 | 8 | 7 | 6 | 5 |
| **START** | 1 | 2 | 3 | 4 |

57

# STEALTH

How quickly can you pass through the maze to complete your mission? Set a timer and then begin – watch out for enemies in your path!

**START**

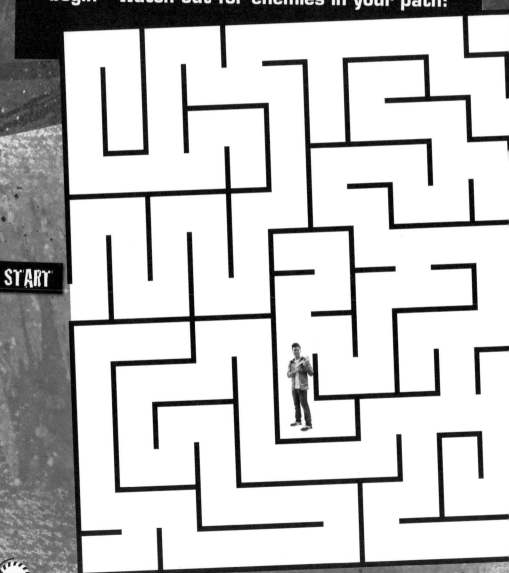

# MISSION

FINISH

Answer on page 127

# SPOT THE DART

When you're in battle, choosing the correct darts is key! Can you spot the odd dart out in the image below?

# ADD YOUR ACCESSORY

Customise these blasters with some awesome accessories!

# MAKE YOUR OWN TARGETS

To test your blasting skills you need targets! Colour in and decorate these targets before cutting them out and placing them around a playing area. Grab some friends and see who can blast the highest score!

20

5

5

10

10

15

15

# SUDOKU

Can you complete the grid so that no one blaster is repeated in each section, row or column?

Answer on page 128

# GUESS THE BLASTER

Test your knowledge of Nerf blasters. Can you name the blasters by looking at each picture?

**1.**

_ _ _ _ _ _ _ _ _ _ _ _ _ _ _ _ _ _ _ _ _ _ _ _ _ _ _ _

**2.**

_ _ _ _ _ _ _ _ _ _ _ _ _ _ _ _ _ _ _ _ _ _ _ _

**3.**

_ _ _ _ _ _ _ _ _ _ _ _ _ _ _ _ _ _ _ _ _ _ _ _

Answers on page 128

# FACTS AND STATS

THE DETACHABLE SCOPE HAS A TWO-DART BLASTER

- **ZOMBIE STRIKE**
- **SURVIVAL SYSTEM**
- **SCRAVENGER**
- Length: 83.8cm
- Height: 27.9cm

LEVER-ACTION BLASTER

AN ON/OFF SLAM-FIRE BUTTON CAN FIRE ALL 12 DARTS RAPIDLY!

TARGETING
SCOPE

TACTICAL LIGHT
BARREL
EXTENSION

NERF

SCAVENGER

NERF

NERF

NERF

12

NERF

ZOMBIE
STRIKE
SURVIVAL
SYSTEM • SYSTÈME • SISTEMA

# MEET THE ZOMBIE STRIKE! TEAM

The Zombie Strike team is on a mission to save the world from a zombie apocalypse! It's hard work but they know as a team they can overcome anything. Let's meet them!

## WREX

Wrex is the youngest of the group and doesn't worry too much about the zombies – unless they steal his food! He sometimes gets himself into difficult situations but luckily his speed and agility can help him out of a tight spot.

## MAVERICK

Maverick is the leader of the group and the oldest member of the Strike team. He is always cool, calm and collected under pressure. The rest of the team respect his opinion, even when he sometimes comes up with a zany plan or two!

## RIPLEY

Ripley is a top mechanic – she can fix anything and is your go-to girl for any battle gear modifications. Smart, clever and highly focused, she is always looking to improve her target precision.

## PROF

Prof is the hacker and scientist of the group – he played a key role in discovering that Nerf foam has a debilitating effect on the zombies. He is always filming the team's exploits and uses the footage for his research.

## KEVIN

Kevin is big, strong and very intelligent. If there's a heavy object that needs lifting, give Kevin a call! He may look intimidating but he is always kind and fair, often keeping the peace on the team.

## DEM

Don't mess with Dem! She is always training to be the best and is only ever happy with first place. Dem carries the most blasters of anyone in the group and won't hesitate to use them if a zombie appears!

# ZOMBIE MASKS

Make these creepy zombie masks and then turn to pages 72-73 to play a Zombie Survival game!

1. Carefully cut around the dotted lines to make your zombie masks. If you don't want to cut them out, you could trace them on to a piece of paper or photocopy them. You could even design your own zombie masks!

2. Use a hole punch to make a hole in each side of the mask.

3. Thread some elastic through the holes. Make a knot at each end of the elastic to secure in place.

# ZOMBIE
## SURVIVAL GAME

GRAB YOUR ZOMBIE MASKS AND
BLASTERS AND SEE WHO CAN
SURVIVE THE ZOMBIE APOCALYPSE!

**PLAYERS: 4 or more**

### YOU WILL NEED:

Zombie masks
Paper and pen
A cup
A mascot

### GAME NAMES:

- STRIKE LEADER x1
- STRIKE SERGEANT x1
- STRIKE TASKFORCE
  (AS MANY AS NEEDED)
- CHIEF ZOMBIE x1
- UNDERCOVER ZOMBIE x1
- ZOMBIES (AS MANY
  AS NEEDED)

### HOW TO PLAY

**1.** Copy the game names on to
pieces of paper, fold them up
and place them all in a cup.

**2.** Take it in turns to choose a
character – if you choose the
undercover zombie, don't tell
anyone else! Pretend you are a
normal zombie.

**3.** The Strike team must take the
mascot and hide it in their HQ.
The mascot must be protected
from zombies at all times!

**4.** Spread out in your playing area
and then begin!

**5.** The zombies must try and capture
the mascot to take over the Strike
team HQ.

The undercover zombie's
job is to help the Strike
team without any of the
other zombies realising!

72

The zombies are on the attack and the Strike team need to act fast! Finish the scene below to find out who wins.

# FACTS AND STATS

**LASER OPS PRO DELTABURST**

Length: 66.8cm

Height: 22.6cm

THE QUICK-RELOAD BUTTON REPLENISHES SUPPLIES OF AMMO!

CUSTOMISABLE

**TEAM INDICATOR: SELECT TO FACE OFF IN A TEAM OR CHOOSE A FREE-FOR-ALL!**

**INDICATORS DISPLAY HEALTH, AMMO LEVELS AND TEAM SELECTION**

DELTABURST

**LIGHT AND SOUND EFFECTS**

# FACTS AND STATS

**LASER OPS PRO ALPHAPOINT**

Length: 28.9cm
Height: 19.1cm

EVERY HIT IS REGISTERED WITH LIGHTS AND SOUND EFFECTS!

ADJUST FOR THE ENVIRONMENT WITH THE INDOORS/ OUTDOORS SWITCH!

**TRACK
PERFORMANCE**

**DETECT ENEM**

ALPHAPOINT

# BATTLE TACTICS

Laser Ops DeltaBurst and AlphaPoint blasters' displays indicate health and ammo levels. Do you think this would affect your tactics in battle? Write your Laser Ops tactics below!

# ENERGY BOOST

In order to be the best in battle you need to have lots of energy. This delicious smoothie will make sure you don't tire when taking on an enemy!

## YOU WILL NEED:

200ml milk (you can use dairy-free alternatives)

One banana

One teaspoon of honey

Three tablespoons of oats

### MAKES ONE LARGE SMOOTHIE

1. Put all the ingredients in a blender.

2. Ask an adult to help you put the lid on the blender and blend until well mixed.

3. Pour into a tall glass and enjoy!

# GAME TIME

You've read about all of the awesome Nerf blasters, now it's time to battle! Use this space to make up some new games to play with your friends.

82

# DOUBLE

Copy the drawing of the Laser Ops Pro AlphaPoint square by square into the grid on the right. Then colour it in!

# TROUBLE

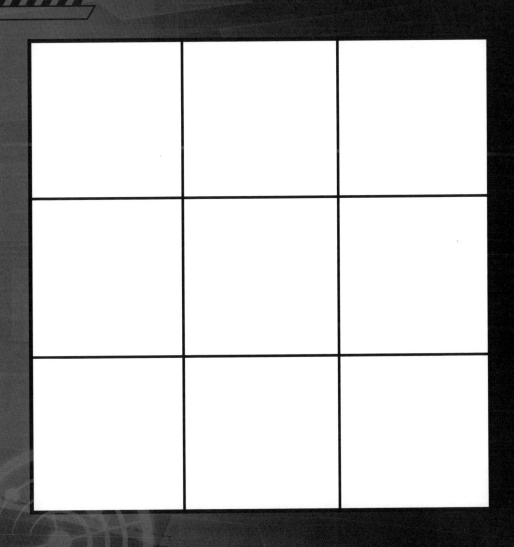

It's time for an epic battle! Can you draw in some extra teammates to help out each team? What blasters will the new players have?

# RIVAL READY

# FRIEND OR

# FOE?

Look at the two images of this team. They look the same, but are they? Can you spot six differences between the photos?

Answers on page 128

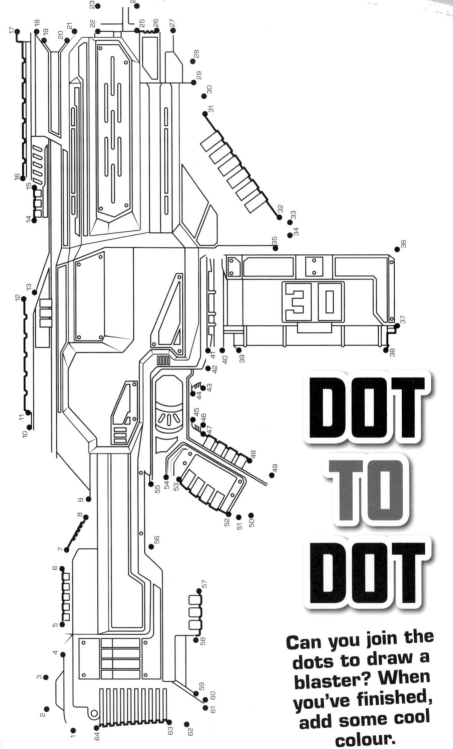

# DOT TO DOT

**Can you join the dots to draw a blaster? When you've finished, add some cool colour.**

# BLASTER CROSSWORD

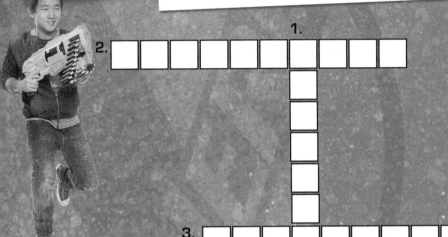

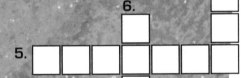

## ACROSS

2. Complete this blaster name – Zombie Strike Survival System …
3. This blaster has light beam targeting
5. This blaster's drum can be reloaded in battle

## DOWN

1. This type of blaster includes the Elite Surgefire, Elite Disruptor and Elite Stryfe
4. This type of blaster monitors ammo and health
6. This blaster has a 6-dart rotating drum

Answers on page 128

# OBSTACLE COURSE

Challenging yourself and your friends is all part of the fun of a Nerf battle! Use the space below to plot out an obstacle course for your next battle.

Will it be indoors or outdoors?

Think about objects to hide behind

Don't forget to think about safe zones and escape routes

You could go around, over or even under objects!

Will the course be individually timed or a race?

# TEST YOUR KNOWLEDGE!

Now you've read about all the cool new blasters, test your memory!

## Q1 NAME THIS BLASTER

## Q2 WHICH BLASTER WOULD BE USED BY THE STRIKE TEAM?

- ☐ Laser Ops Delta Burst
- ☐ N-Strike Elite Disruptor
- ☐ Zombie Strike Survival System Scravenger

## Q3 COMPLETE THE NAME OF THIS BLASTER – N-STRIKE MEGA ACCUSTRIKE ...

- ☐ Thunderhawk
- ☐ Thundereagle
- ☐ Lightningstrike

## Q4 WHICH OFFERS ONE-HANDED BLASTING?

- ☐ Delta Trooper
- ☐ N-Strike Elite Stryfe Blaster
- ☐ Laser Ops AlphaPoint

## Q5 THE ZOMBIE STRIKE SURVIVAL SYSTEM SCRAVENGER HAS AN ON/OFF SLAM-FIRE BUTTON

☐ True
☐ False

## Q6 WHICH BLASTER COMES WITH MEGA WHISTLER DARTS?

☐ N-Strike Mega Cycloneshock
☐ Modulus Mediator
☐ Infinus

## Q7 WHICH BLASTER IS FULLY MOTORISED?

☐ Laser Ops Delta Burst
☐ Mega Tri-Break
☐ N-Strike Elite Infinus

## Q8 THE LASER OPS ALPHAPOINT REGISTERS HITS WITH LIGHTS AND SOUNDS

☐ True
☐ False

Answers on page 128

# IN THE SHADOWS

**These players are ready for battle but to avoid detection they always stay in the shadows! Can you match up the players and their shadows?**

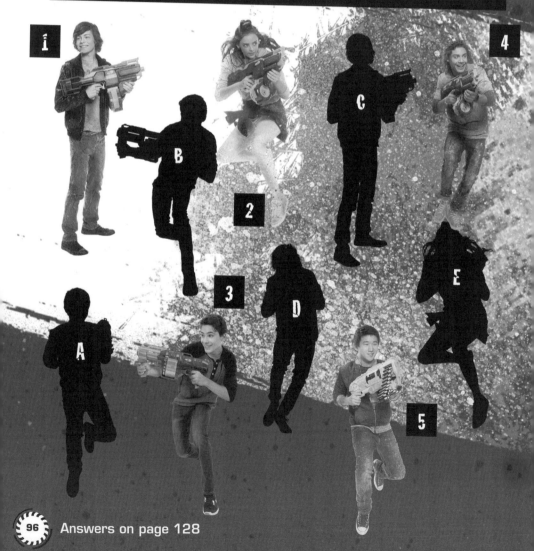

# NERF

# BLAST OR BUST

# BLAST OR BUST

Cut out the cards on the following pages and divide them evenly between players. Each player picks the top card of their pile. Take it in turns to pick a category and read out a stat. Whoever has the blaster with the best stat, wins the card. The player who ends up with all the cards wins!

## N-STRIKE MODULUS MEDIATOR

Length: 35.6cm

Height: 22.9cm

Fire Power: ●●●○○

Look: ●●●●○

## N-STRIKE MEGA CYCLONESHOCK

Length: 41.2cm

Height: 25.3cm

Fire Power: ●●●●○

Look: ●●○○○

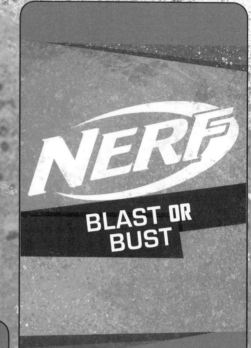

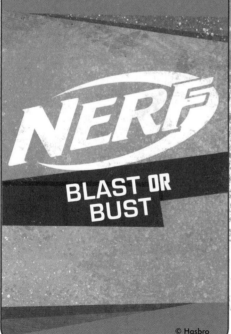

## N-STRIKE MEGA ACCUSTRIKE THUNDERHAWK

Length: 1 metre

Height: 39.1cm

Fire Power: ●●●●○

Look: ●●●●●

## N-STRIKE ELITE QUADRANT

Length: 22.9cm

Height: 16.5cm

Fire Power: ●●○○○

Look: ●●●●○

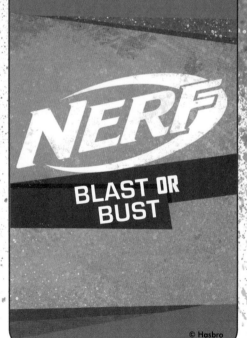

## N-STRIKE ELITE INFINUS

Length: 64.5cm

Height: 34.8cm

Fire Power: ●●●●○

Look: ●●○○○

## N-STRIKE ELITE SURGEFIRE

Length: 45.7cm

Height: 20.3cm

Fire Power: ●●●●●

Look: ●●●○○

© Hasbro

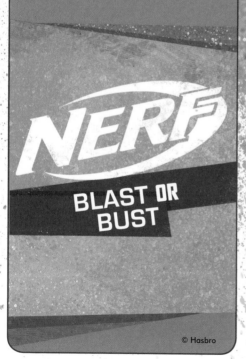

© Hasbro

## N-STRIKE ELITE DISRUPTOR

Length: 31.5cm

Height: 22cm

Fire Power: ●●●○○

Look: ●●●●●○

## N-STRIKE ELITE DELTA TROOPER

Length: 69.5cm

Height: 25.4cm

Fire Power: ●●○○○

Look: ●●●●●

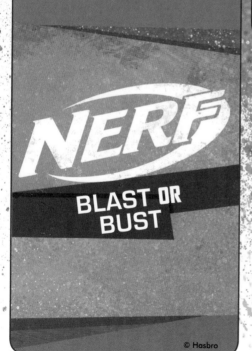

## N-STRIKE ELITE FIRESTRIKE

Length: 31.5cm

Height: 22cm

Fire Power:

Look: ●●●●●●

## N-STRIKE ELITE STRYFE

Length: 33cm

Height: 17.8cm

Fire Power:

Look:

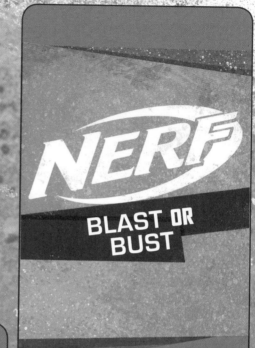

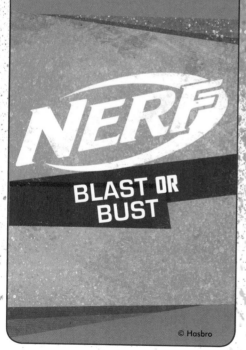

## ZOMBIE STRIKE SURVIVAL SYSTEM SCRAVENGER

Length: 83.8cm

Height: 27.9cm

Fire Power: ●●●○○

Look: ●●●●●

## LASER OPS PRO DELTABURST

Length: 66.8cm

Height: 22.6cm

Fire Power: ●●●●○

Look: ●●●○○

## LASER OPS PRO ALPHAPOINT

Length: 28.9cm

Height: 19.1cm

Fire Power: ●●○○○

Look: ●●●●●●

## N-STRIKE MEGA TRI-BREAK

Length: 31.8cm

Height: 22.9cm

Fire Power: ●●●○○

Look: ●●●○○

# SCORING SHEETS

Use the following pages to keep score of all the games you play with your friends. Who is the ultimate Nerf champion?

# SCORING SHEETS

# SCORING SHEETS

# SCORING SHEETS

# SCORING SHEETS

# SCORING SHEETS

# SCORING SHEETS

# SCORING SHEETS

# SCORING SHEETS

# SCORING SHEETS

# SCORING SHEETS

# SCORING SHEETS

# SCORING SHEETS

# SCORING SHEETS

# ANSWERS

## PAGES 26-27

## PAGE 32

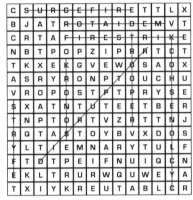

| C | S | U | R | G | E | F | I | R | E | T | T | L | X |
|---|---|---|---|---|---|---|---|---|---|---|---|---|---|
| B | J | A | T | R | O | T | A | I | D | E | M | V | T |
| C | R | T | A | F | I | R | E | S | T | R | I | K | E |
| N | B | T | P | O | P | Z | I | P | R | A | T | C | T |
| T | K | X | E | K | G | V | E | W | O | S | A | O | X |
| A | S | R | Y | R | O | N | P | T | O | U | C | H | U |
| V | R | O | P | O | S | T | B | T | P | R | Y | S | E |
| S | X | A | T | N | T | U | T | E | E | T | B | E | R |
| T | N | P | T | O | R | T | V | Z | R | T | T | N | J |
| R | Q | T | A | S | T | O | Y | B | V | X | D | O | S |
| Y | L | T | I | E | M | N | A | R | Y | T | U | L | F |
| F | T | O | T | P | E | I | F | N | U | I | Q | C | N |
| E | K | L | T | R | U | R | W | Q | U | W | E | Y | A |
| T | X | I | Y | K | R | E | U | T | A | B | L | C | R |

## PAGE 33

## PAGE 48

MEET ME AT SUNSET

## PAGE 49

1. 35.6cm
2. N-Strike Mega AccuStrike
   Thunderhawk
3. N-Strike Elite Stryfe
4. True

## PAGES 58-59

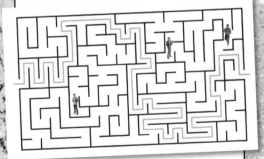

## PAGE 60

**SPOT THE DART**

When you're in battle, choosing the correct darts is key! Can you spot the odd dart out in the image below?

## PAGE 64

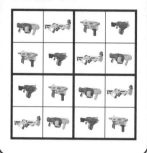

## PAGE 89

## PAGE 65

1. N-Strike Modulus Mediator
2. N-Strike Mega Cycloneshock
3. Laser Ops DeltaBurst

## PAGE 91

```
2. S C R A V E N G E R
        T
        R              4.
        I              L
        K              A
3. F I R E S T R I K E S
                       R
                6.     O
                D      P
5. I N F I N U S
                S
                R
                U
                P
                T
                O
                R
```

## PAGES 94-95

1. N-Strike Elite Delta Trooper
2. Zombie Strike Survival System Scravenger
3. Thunderhawk
4. N-Strike Elite Stryfe Blaster
5. False
6. N-Strike Mega Cycloneshock
7. N-Strike Elite Infinus
8. True

## PAGE 96

1-C
2-E
3-B
4-D
5-A